The Creamy Craft of Cosmetic Making

with Essential Oils and Their Friends

By

Jan Benham

Author of
The Baby Boomers Beauty Bible
& The Little Book of lipsticks

The Creamy Craft of Cosmetic Making with Essential Oils and their Friends.

Second edition

Published by:
The Aroma Shoppe Ltd.
Toronto, Canada

Also by Jan Benham
The Baby Boomers Beauty Bible, 2010, 2004
The Little Book of Lipsticks, 2010

Interior photography by Bob Burch and Jan Benham

ISBN: 978-1-907571-19-0

Printed and bound in Great Britain by
CPI Antony Rowe, Chippenham and Eastbourne

Acknowledgements

I would like to thank people who have inspired me in the past: Shirley Price who told me that I could achieve and be anything I wanted in life, and my mother who encouraged me onto this path.

My friends and colleagues, especially Danielle Murray, Violet A. Cordy, Rani M Johnson, Doctor Helena Ovens, and clients with whom over the years have supported me in my quest.

My Japanese students and friends, especially Eri Nose and Tomoko Yamaji

I would also like to thank Don Lamoreux for his help in the editing of the first edition of this book. My son Glyn for his help in the Canadian store and school.

And finally to Jan Kloosterhuis with love.

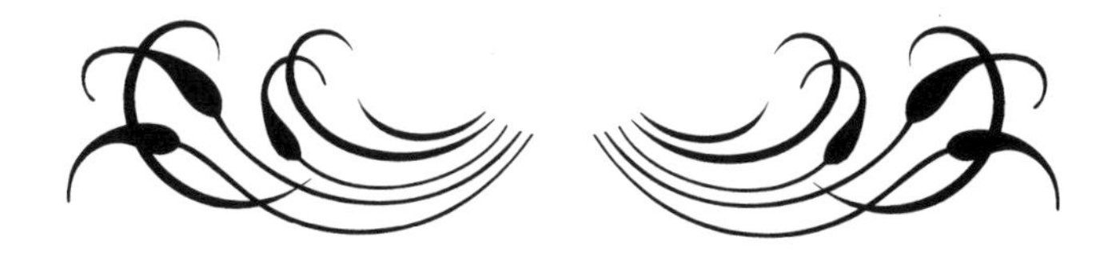

About the Author

Jan Benham is the President of the Institute of Aromatherapy and Aroma Shoppe. She has been a holistic therapist, practicing and teaching for over twenty years. Jan taught Aromatherapy for Shirley Price in the early 80's, one of the pioneers and founders of aromatherapy in the UK.

Jan is a fellow member of the Society of Health and Beauty Therapists UK, member of the International Federation of Holistic Therapists UK, member of the International Federation of Professional Aromatherapists, UK, a Registered Aromatherapy Health Practitioner with the Canadian Examining Board of Health Care Practitioners and past President of the Canadian Federation of Aromatherapists.

Jan owns schools in Canada and the UK, and offers various workshops including: cosmetic making, aromatherapy, and Aroma Cosmetology - Holistic Skin Care. Her Certified Natural Health Practitioner Courses are known all over the world.

Jan is also a tutor at the Shirley Price College in the UK and New Directions Aromatics.

Jan is the author of books about all-natural and holistic cosmetics: *The Baby Boomers Beauty Bible, 2004* (now in its second edition), *The Little Book of Lipsticks), 2010, Successful Soap* (currently in press) and is currently working on her fourth book: *The Mineral Makeup Manual* (coming soon!).

As well as being an author and a consultant, Jan regularly gives press, TV and radio interviews, and contributes to journals and magazines.

Contents

PART FOUR

BODY CARE

PART FIVE

La pièce de résistance

Preface to the Second edition

Welcome to the revised edition of the Creamy Craft of Cosmetic making with essential oils and their friends.

The first edition, published in 1996, although fifteen years old, is still current and subsequently very few changes have had to be made to the 2nd edition.

This book, although using the elements and accumulated knowledge of aromatherapy, is focused on natural skin care and cream making. Consequently, I have included the aromatic essential oils that are most useful for skin care.

These essential oils, as well as having therapeutic effects on the skin, also play an important role in holistic health care. For further information on this aspect on Holistic Aromatherapy, you can read any number of books such as *The Art or Aromatherapy* by Robert Tisserand and the *Aromatherapy Workbook* by Shirley Price.

As a practicing aromatherapist and cosmetologist since 1978, I have been appalled at the lack of 'unclean' skin creams available on the market. Aromatherapists require the use of pure unscented creams and lotions in making up home treatments for their clientele. We can use plain almond oil to mix the aromatherapy blends in, but it is not always convenient or desirable for the client to put oil on his or her body or face. Thus, it is useful to be able to put the client's special blend of essential oils into a cream or lotion.

Unfortunately due to the lack of pure unscented creams and lotions, some of my colleagues have had to resort to buying pharmaceutical grade base creams from pharmacists. These creams and lotions contain mineral oils and synthetic preservatives, and have no place amongst aromatherapy.

Conversely, vegetable oils are highly penetrative able to carry the essential oils to the dermis and into the blood stream.

Over the years I have developed and produced creams and lotions. The recipes are very straight forward and easy to follow, and, as long as you are patient, the results will be rewarding. After making the base creams and lotions, you can mix in the essential oils to your heart's delight. For mixing and blending, I have included some recipes that I have used on myself and clients over the years. Do not limit yourselves to the ingredients listed; there is much more to be discovered. At the back of the book, I have left a few pages to record your very own personal cream making history. My hope with this book is to get you started on this wonderful world of cosmetic making. Experiment, be creative and above all have fun.

For further reading, '*the Baby Boomer's Beauty Bible'* was published in 2004 *(a revised edition in 2010),* this book focuses on natural shampoo making and deodorants, and gives additional recipes and treatments for skin care, especially for neck firming, anti-ageing, rosacea and acne.

Jan Benham

PART ONE the Essentials Good Guys Versus Bad Guys

Western medical practitioners, except for a few enlightened exceptions, still regard the human body as a car and discuss problems and solutions in mechanical terms. If the human being is not working properly, for example, the solution is to find and change the defective part or in some way modify it. In reaction to this mechanistic medicine, there has been a phenomenal growth in holistic alternatives.

How do the above limitations of Western medicine relate to natural skin care? The pharmaceutical and big business cosmetic companies along with their servants in the medical profession try to synthesize and duplicate what already occurs in nature. The sticky debate is that in a living organism there is something more than the sum of its component parts. Whether we are discussing a human being or a naturally occurring plant product, there is always a "life force" energy that is present. The scientific community resists any attempt to link itself with this sort of mysticism. It is willing to consider the merits of Chinese medicine for example, but rejects any "mystical mumbo jumbo" discussion of yin and yang energies. Similarly, it rejects holistic approaches to health care.

Modern science is so technologically oriented that to remind it of its primitive roots is as frightening as a social climber meeting one of his old neighborhood friends at an elegant dinner party. The cosmetic industry seems to forget its origins from Galen's cold cream.

How did the cosmetic industry become so alienated from nature? It got seduced by the easy availability of petroleum by-products and their ability to be patented. Not only are these by-products less effective in skin care treatment, there is mounting evidence that they break down collagen in the skin. Thus, the vicious irony here is that many synthetic anti-ageing products directly contribute to the ageing process of the skin itself. With this problem, we can add the harmful effects of synthetic dyes and preservatives. (e.g. formaldehyde, and parabens). *For more information, see the chapter on politically incorrect ingredients for natural cosmetics.*

In contrast to commercial ready-made cosmetics, the homemade ones offered in these pages make exclusive use of natural substances. They contain no mineral oils, animal products in any form i.e. lanolin or gelatin, synthetic substances, synthetic preservatives or dyes.

So that we do not also lose sight of the roots of skin care, let us start with a review of the essential essences, so to speak.

General history and all that stuff

or

What did Cleopatra know?

Since our records from Atlantis are still a little vague, Egypt figures as the beginning of our "essential" story. Essential oils in ancient Egypt were used in healing, in temple rituals, for perfumes and embalming.

As in the story of the Magi, frankincense and myrrh were highly prized in ancient Egypt. They were especially useful in embalming as they kill bacteria. Cleopatra is popularly associated with expensive perfumes and cosmetics. Many tales and legends exist about her extravagances in this area. To move from the legendary to the factual, however, there are records of the use of kohl, henna and essential oils by the Egyptians of the middle and upper classes. Egypt was close to the trade routes of the far East and in a position to be aware of developments in this area.

In the middle Ages, perfumes and cosmetics were often used to mask the unhygienic conditions of the era. As the power of the Catholic Church waned, there was a rush to emulate the ideals of the Greco-Roman eras, in terms of bathing and adorning the body which had hitherto been forbidden under religious edicts.

The use of herbs became more widespread and what was useful became more apparent. The growth of the middle class in the 19th century is also one reason that increased the demand for inexpensive effective home remedies.

The use of herbs became more widespread and what was useful became more apparent. The growth of the middle class in the 19th century is also one reason that increased the demand for inexpensive effective home remedies.

Essential oils have been used for centuries for healing and perfumes, while the following people helped to bring essential oils and aromatherapy to the twentieth century.

Gattafosse a chemist around the turn of the century discovered the healing properties of lavender oil after burning his hand in a laboratory accident which led to a life long research on essential oils and their properties. "Aromatherapie: Les huiles essentielles hormones vegetales", the first book on aromatherapy, was published by Gattefosse in 1937.

Dr. Jean Valnet developed the use of essential oils for internal use, practiced by medical doctors in France. Dr. Valnet wrote the book "The Practice of Aromatherapy". Modern day phyto aromatherapy is the grandfather of Dr. Valnet's studies.

Madame Maury, the mother of modern aromatherapy developed the field of the use of essential oils via massage and smell. She was the inspiration for Shirley Price, Daniele Ryman and other pioneers in aromatherapy. Madame Maury's "Guide to Aromatherapy", was first published in the French language in 1961.

The English have gone the route of **Holistic** Aromatherapy (external use with massage), whilst the French have gone into **Clinical** Aromatherapy (internal use of essential oils).

Essential Oils The Holy Grail of Cosmetics

Essential oils are odorous and highly volatile (they readily evaporate in the open air). They are extracted by various methods, usually by steam distillation from plants, herbs, flowers, seeds, grasses, roots, trees and fruits. Different essential oils can be extracted from various parts of one plant. In the case of the Orange tree, **Petitgrain** essential oil is extracted from the leaves, **Orange** essential oil is extracted from the rind of the fruit and **Neroli,** sometimes called Orange blossom is extracted from the blossom. These essential oils, even though they are from the same tree, have different aromas and different therapeutic qualities. Often described as the 'life force' of the plant; I like to think of essential oils as 'my genie in the bottle'. Essential oils used in natural skin care are the results of collective knowledge gained over thousands of years from many contributing countries. Their marvelous therapeutic properties, together with their medicinal capabilities, are known and recognized all over the world. All essential oils are anti-bacterial, and many of them are anti-viral and anti-fungal.

Essential oils are natural and achieve the desired results that cannot be gained through the use of synthetics because essential oils can be classed as ***biotic*** **(Strengthens living tissue whilst destroying bacteria), which is the opposite of anti-biotic.**

This explains the success of natural essence in the healing process

Essential oil therapy, also known as ***Aromatherapy,*** works directly on the skin and organs, and has a direct effect on the limbic system in the brain. For example, the smell of ylang ylang stimulates the pituitary gland, which then releases a sexually stimulating neurochemical, endorphin. Just smelling Marjoram, can cause drowsiness which is helpful in the treatment of insomnia and can also tame an overactive sex drive. Neroli, by aroma alone, can help in cases of sudden shock, grief and hysteria. Essential oils work on all levels. In massage they penetrate the skin and reach the blood stream in minute quantities to heal our muscles and organs at the same time we are receiving their scents through the nose. It appears that they can activate part of the brain which stores memories and that they also have an effect on the nervous system so that they can help to reduce anxiety for instance without the side effects of chemical tranquilizers. To sum up, essential oils work both psychologically and physiologically and by affecting the state of the mind, the state of the body may be altered.

Jan distilling lavender essential oil

There are three styles of Aromatherapy that have developed over the years:

1. **Holistic Aromatherapy** is a hand's on therapy employing essential oils and massage. Nutrition and subtle energy imbalances (mental state) are also taken into consideration
2. **Medical (Clinical) Aromatherapy** uses essential oils internally as drugs and/or medication. Many doctors in France practice this form of therapy.
3. **Aesthetic Aromatherapy** is used specifically for beauty treatments, skin problems and cellulite reduction.

Uses of Essential oils

Essential oils are very concentrated and should be used with care. Apart from a few exceptions, they should NOT BE USED NEAT directly on the skin but dissolved in vegetable oil, alcohol or water.

Internally (ingested)

Take 3 drops of ***pure high quality*** essential oil in honey and hot water up to 3 times a day for a maximum of 3 weeks. The body builds up a tolerance to the oil after 3 weeks. You may also take it on a sugar cube. The formula is 3 drops, 3 times a day for 3 weeks, stop, for 3 weeks and then you may start again.

Tea: 1 - 2 drops in water or 3 - 4 drops on a tea bag.

There are some essential oils that should never be taken internally: pennyroyal *(can be fatal),* sage, wintergreen and many others. Never ingest essential oils unless under the guidance of a professional practitioner.

Inhalation

1. Add up to 10 drops on a tissue and breathe deeply.
2. Add 6 - 10 drops of essential oil/s to a bowl of steaming water, cover head with towel, close eyes and breathe in vapours for several minutes.

Steaming with the appropriate essential oils for skin care is excellent for facial cleansing but not for those with sensitive skin.

Baths (foot, sitz or body)

Fill the bath with warm water, add 6 - 10 drops of essential oil (or a blend), stir surface and soak for at least 10 minutes, allowing the oils to penetrate the skin while inhaling the vapours. Essential oils can be diluted in fractionated coconut oil and added to bath water to moisturise the skin as you relax. For optimum benefit follow with a massage.

Massage or application

Add 15 - 30 drops to 50ml carrier oil or lotion. (For a single application, add 2 - 3 drops to one teaspoon of carrier oil or lotion).

Vegetable oils are the best to use for maximum penetration. They must be pure, fine and cold pressed, with little or no smell. The basic rule is the more expensive the oil, usually the better the quality. Sweet almond oil, jojoba, fractionated coconut and grapeseed are the best as they are light, have little odour and are suitable for all skin types.

For physical problems, use maximum dose; for psychological problems, use the minimum dose.

Compresses These can be hot /or cold.

Add 10 drops of essential oils to a bowl of water. Soak a cloth in the blend of essential oils and water, wring the cloth and then apply to the affected area of the body.

If using alternative hot and cold compresses, start with hot and finish with cold.

Use less i.e. 1 - 2 drops for a baby. To reduce fever use a Eucalyptus compress, and apply the cloth to the forehead.

Perfumes

Essential oils were first used over 4,000 years ago by the Egyptians as perfumes; today, most perfumes are synthetic.

Jasmine, Ylang Ylang, Rose, Neroli, Sandalwood, and Patchouli are perfect perfumes by themselves, or blended with citrus essential oils such as Bergamot, Orange, Lime, and Lemon.

Use 1 drop of the exotic scents to approximately 6 drops of citrus essential oils.

Room spray

Fill a plant sprayer with water and add a few drops of essential oil/s. Shake vigorously before use. Oils can be diluted in a little alcohol before adding water. *Avoid spraying on polished surfaces.*

Neat application

Apply 1 drop undiluted onto blemishes i.e. zits and boils *(Lavender),* cold sores *(Lavender and/or Bergamot)*, Bruises *(Cypress),* burns *(Lavender)* and for the relief of insect bites and stings *(Geranium).*

Cautions:

- Essential oils should never be used neat on the skin except as for the above.
- Do not take essential oils internally unless under the guidance of a qualified practitioner.
- Keep essential oils away from children and pets.
- Avoid eye area.
- Check for contra indications to any oils for specific conditions such as pregnancy and sunbathing.
- Essential oils are flammable, so do not put them on or near a naked flame.
- Essential oils may damage certain plastics and polished wood surfaces.

The Most Useful Essential Oils in Skin Care

This being primarily a cream making book, I have included just those essential oils that are of most use in regard to skin care and likewise just mentioned the properties of those oils accordingly. All these essential oils have many other properties e.g. for pain relief, muscle spasm, high and low blood pressure, digestive disorders, and asthma.

BENZOIN RESINOID (*Styrax benzoin*)

Benzoin is a resinoid derived through extraction from the resin of a tree native to Asia.

The oil is antiseptic, soothing to the skin, and heals wounds, infections and abscesses. It can be used for chapped skin, redness, and itching *(helpful for eczema).*

BERGAMOT *(Citrus bergamia)*

The essential oil of Bergamot is obtained by expression, simple pressure on the rind of the fruit. Bergamot can be used for all skin types and with its antiseptic and healing properties; it makes a good choice for treating disorders such as acne, eczema and psoriasis.

A hot compress of bergamot and eucalyptus can be used on boils to draw out the infection. Do not use bergamot undiluted as it can cause skin irritation. Bergamot can be used in bath oils, deodorants (being slightly astringent), and perfumes. *Trivia*, bergamot is an ingredient in *Earl Grey Tea.*

CARROT SEED *(Daucus carota)*

This essential oil is known to help with mature, ageing skin, wrinkles, psoriasis and eczema.

CHAMOMILE
German chamomile (Matricaria chamomilla)
Roman chamomile (Anthemis nobilis)

There are two types of chamomile that I like to work with. One is known as Roman chamomile and the other is known as German chamomile. Both are distilled from the flowers and the leaves. The color varies from the light blue of Roman chamomile to the dark blue of German chamomile.

Roman chamomile, because of its antiseptic, vaso constricting and healing properties, is used for sensitive, dry, reddened or itchy skin, acne, rashes and for the treatment of broken blood vessels on the face. It also helps skin allergies when added to a cream or oil.

German chamomile differs from Roman chamomile in that it contains higher proportions of azulene which gives German chamomile its dark blue color. Azulene is effective against infections and accelerates the healing process.

CEDARWOOD *(Juniperus virginiana)*

Cedarwood essential oil is distilled from the twigs and wood of the tree. Cedarwood was valued highly by the ancient Egyptians and was used in the embalming and mummification process. They also valued it highly as an ingredient for cosmetics.

In skin care, Cedarwood is valuable for all types of skin eruptions such as acne, eczema, psoriasis and dermatitis due to its antiseptic and astringent properties. (Note, in high concentrations it will irritate the skin). It has other uses in the treatment of greasy hair and dandruff.

CLARY SAGE *(Salvia sclarea)*

Clary sage is distilled from the flowers of a herb that grows in Southern Europe. It has an estrogen like effect on the skin making it useful for preventing premature ageing of the skin. Its versatility makes it effective with hydrated, infected and other skin types. Clary sage will also reduce the excessive production of sebum especially on the scalp so is useful as a hair tonic for people with very greasy hair or dandruff. In addition, clary sage will help skin disorders such as spots and boils.

CYPRESS *(Cupressus sempervirens)*

The essential oil of cypress is distilled from the leaves and cones of the cypress tree.

This is wonderful for the face as it smooth's and tightens the skin. It is particularly useful for firming the skin on the neck and around the eyes

Caution: Do not use undiluted on the skin, especially close to the eyes. Follow the recipe guidelines.

It has vasoconstriction properties, so it is used for the treatment of broken blood vessels on the face and varicose veins on the legs. Cypress helps in the care of greasy, hydrated, slack, tired and sluggish skin.

FENNEL *(Foeniculum vulgare)*

Fennel essential oil, extracted from the fennel seeds, acts as a natural diuretic. Since it contains phyto-hormones which act as a natural estrogen, it combats ageing problems such as wrinkles, loose skin and cellulite. Fennel is also important in gum treatment.

FRANKINCENSE *(Boswellia carteri)*

Frankincense essential oil which comes from the boswellia tree, is extracted from the resin of the bark by steam distillation. Frankincense has been used for thousands of years and was used in ancient Egypt for skin care.

Frankincense is astringent, rejuvenating and extremely beneficial to the skin, helping to preserve a youthful complexion, preventing wrinkles and other abominations of old age. Frankincense has a definite tonic effect on the skin, helping to restore some tone to slack looking facial skin while slowing down the appearance of wrinkles and reducing wrinkles that have already formed.

GERANIUM *(Pelargonium graveolens)*

The essential oil of geranium obtained by distillation from the leaves has a cleansing, refreshing and astringent effect on the skin and is recommended for general skin care. It may be also used on inflamed skin and is used for sluggish oily skin types. Because of its balancing effect on the sebaceous production in the skin, geranium is valuable for skin that is excessively dry or oily.

GRAPEFRUIT *(Citrus paradisi)*

This is obtained by cold expression of the peel of the fruit. Grapefruit is non-toxic and non-irritating, and is effective for the treatment of acne and oily skin. A lymphatic stimulant, it is helpful for obesity, cellulitis and water retention. Use regularly in baths and massage.

HO WOOD/LEAF *(Cinnamomum camphora).*

Ho wood has taken the place of Rosewood *(see below for more discussion).* Due to its chemical constituent, it has similar effects on the skin as Lavender. Ho wood is antibacterial and antifungal, helping conditions such as acne, itchy or inflamed skin and wrinkles. Although used in general skin care, because of its antimicrobial properties, it is useful for the treatment of fungal conditions such as athlete's foot.

The replacement of Rosewood by the Ho leaf/wood has generated some controversy and confusion. Ho leaf/wood has been characterized as toxic. Ho leaf/wood oil is not toxic although there are several species of Ho; cineole, camphor, and linalol types, which are considered to be potentially hazardous. Confusion arises due to similarities in botanical nomenclature. (Ho and Camphor both read as *Cinnamomum camphora.*) The Ho to use is of the linalol type which has a total linalol content similar to that found in rosewood oil, and is considered one of the safer oils.

In regards to the ecological problems, Rosewood (*Aniba rosaedora)* has been classified as an endangered species by the species unit at the world Conservation Monitoring Centre in Cambridge, U.K

JUNIPER BERRY *(Juniperus communis)*

Juniper berry essential oil is distilled from the berries. Juniper is antiseptic, antibacterial, toning and detoxifying, useful in all disorders of the skin and blood. It also helps tissue repair and inhibits infection.

Other uses include for the care of oily, hydrated or sluggish skin and in the treatment of acne, psoriasis, eczema and cellulite.

LAVENDER *(Lavendula officinalis and Lavendula angustifolia.)*

The essential oil of lavender is distilled from the flowers and stalks of the plant.

The soothing, antiseptic and anti-inflammatory properties of lavender make it valuable for many skin conditions, and its well loved aroma lends itself to blending in creams and lotions. Lavender will also stimulate the growth of healthy new cells making it effective for cracked skin, eczema, boils, wounds and burns. It is helpful for acne as it inhibits the bacteria which causes the skin infection while soothing the skin, helping to balance the over secretion of sebum.

LEMON *(Citrus limonum)*

Lemon essential oil is derived from the peel. It is a good friend to the skin especially for problems of excess oil and acne. A very important use for aging baby boomers is the ability to tighten and stimulate the skin. For the body, it stimulates the lymphatic circulation which helps conditions such as cellulite, obesity and water retention.

LEMONGRASS *(Cymbopogon citratus)*

Lemongrass derived from a grass native to India is astringent and a tonic for the skin making it useful for the treatment of oily skin and open pores. Lemongrass is also used as an insect repellent and in natural flea collars for cats.

LIME *(Citrus aurantifolia)*

Lime is obtained by the cold expression of the peel and is a refreshing tonic for the skin. It helps to stimulate the lymphatic system helping conditions such as obesity, cellulitis and water retention.

MYRRH *(Commiphora myrrha)*

Myrrh is extracted from a desert tree that grows in the Middle East. Its thick reddish-brown oil is obtained through extraction and distillation of its resin.

The three wise men knew a thing or two about myrrh as it was widely used by the Egyptians in embalming. Myrrh oil is rejuvenating, fungicidal, anti-inflammatory, antiseptic, cooling and astringent.

NEROLI *(Citrus aurantium)*

Also known as Orange blossom, Neroli is extracted from the blossoms of the bitter orange tree. Neroli is particularly valuable in skin care, for it has the special property of stimulating the growth of healthy new cells, with certain special rejuvenating effects. It can be used for all skin types, but is especially good for dry and sensitive skins.

ORANGE SWEET *(Citrus aurantium)*

Orange is obtained by the cold expression of the peel of the fruit and is effective for dull and oily skins as well as for general skin care. It helps to stimulate the lymphatic system which helps conditions such as obesity, cellulite, and water retention.

ROSE *(Rosa damascena and Rosa Centifolia)*

Here we have one of the most valuable commodities on the perfume and essential oil market. Rose oil is extracted by varying methods, depending on the country of origin. The finest rose oil and the most costly is from Bulgaria known as Bulgaria Rose Otto, extracted from the Damask rose.

Rose oil is a highly effective ingredient in natural skin care products. It is anti-inflammatory, astringent, toning and rejuvenating, helping most skin problems including: eczema, dry, sensitive and mature skin.

ROSEMARY *(Rosmarinus officinalis)*

The essential oil of rosemary is distilled from the entire herb.

Rosemary has been used for skin and hair care for hundreds of years. Due to its rejuvenating effects, rosemary is traditionally used to restore hair loss or color. Because of its astringent and antiseptic properties, rosemary oil stimulates the circulation and metabolism of the skin.

SANDALWOOD *(Santalum album)*

Sandalwood is distilled from the heartwood of the tree.

As a cosmetic ingredient, sandalwood is beneficial for all skin types. It can be used for dry, dehydrated skin *(warm compresses are particularly good here)*. Conversely, it is helpful for oily skins and acne, as it is slightly astringent and a powerful antiseptic.

YLANG YLANG *(Cananga odorata)*

The essential oil of Ylang ylang is obtained from the flowers of a small tropical tree. *(The name ylang ylang means, flower of flowers.)*

Ylang Ylang is like the Yin/Yang of essential oils for its ability to balance sebaceous glands; it can be used for both dry and oily skins.

Having surveyed the essential oils, here is a look at the carrier substances necessary to make creams, lotions, toners and so on.

Politically Correct Ingredients for Natural Cosmetics

In order to achieve the best quality as possible when making natural cosmetics, it is important to use carrier oils that are cold pressed.

ALMOND OIL, SWEET *(Prunus dulcis)*

Sweet almond oil is extracted from the ripe seeds or sweet almonds of the almond tree. There also exists an essential oil from bitter almonds which is never used in skin care because of the risk of prussic acid forming during distillation.

Sweet almond oil contains both mono - and polyunsaturated fatty acids and vitamins (A, B1, B2 and B6). Because, it has small amounts of Vitamin E, it will keep for longer periods of time and will not easily go rancid. Almond oil penetrates well into the skin, being both nourishing and protecting, it also soothes eczema.

Use: Can be used 100%.

APRICOT KERNEL OIL *(Prunus armeniaca)*

Apricot yields the same oils chemically as almond oil so it has similar effects. It is very light and easily absorbed into the skin. The ancient Russians used apricot oil and found it to have beneficial effects on dry and mature skin.

Use: 100%

ARROWROOT POWDER *(Maranta arundinacea)*

Made from the starch of plants, it was used by the American Indians to heal wounds from poisoned arrows. It can help moisturisers to penetrate the skin. Also it is used as a base for dusting powders.

AVOCADO OIL *(Persea Americana)*

Avocado oil is extracted from the pulp of the avocado pear. It sometimes has a cloudy appearance being even a bit sludgy at the bottom. This should be regarded as a good sign rather than a fault as it indicates that it has not been refined.

Avocado oil contains both saturated and monounsaturated fatty acids with relatively large amounts of vitamins (A, B and D) . It is also rich in lecithin. Avocado has the ability to penetrate the outer layers of the skin, because being similar to sebaceous fat, the oil quickly merges with it. Avocado is valuable for skin care on account of its beneficial effect on dry skin and wrinkles. Its healing properties help to regenerate cells, which is useful in the healing of scarred tissue. Avocado oil soothes eczema and is used in sun preparations on account of its emollient properties.

Use: Up to 25%

BEESWAX

Beeswax, naturally yellow in colour, is extracted from the honeycomb and becomes white on exposure to air.

Beeswax is a natural emulsifying agent that can make creams and lotions either smooth or hard, according to the proportions used. Beeswax, which does not have the ability to penetrate the outer layers of the skin, is recommended as a protective ointment or cream as in lip balms and hand creams.

Use: Percentage varies according to thickness of cream or ointment required.

BORAGE SEED OIL (*Borago officinalis*)

Borage oil is extracted from the seeds.
It is anti-inflammatory being helpful for conditions such as eczema, psoriasis and prematurely aged skin.

Use: Up to 25%.

CALENDULA OIL *(Calendula officinalis)*

Calendula, known as pot marigold, is extracted from the flower heads of the plant. Calendula oil has a favourable effect on the skin in all cosmetic preparations and has been proved highly successful in the healing of chapped and cracked skin. It is also anti-inflammatory and helps to heal bed sores as well as varicose veins and broken capillaries. Because of its amazing healing power, calendula oil has been used in ointments and tinctures throughout Europe and America for hundreds of years.

Use: Up to 25%

CARROT ROOT OIL *(Daucus carota)*

Extraction of this oil requires expert attention so it is not readily available. Carrot oil is an antioxidant, rich in beta-carotene, Vitamins B, C, D and E and essential fatty acids. This oil is especially good for dry, chapped skin and has rejuvenating properties, delaying the ageing process.

Beneficial as a natural preservative in creams and lotions, it is also used for colouring.

Use: 5%. *Note: Only a few drops of carrot oil is generally needed.*

CLAY

The healing properties of clay have been known for centuries. Clay is extremely absorbent, drawing out toxins and impurities from the skin; clay is also antiseptic, anti-inflammatory and is stimulating to the circulation. Clay contains a very high percentage of silica and other minerals such a magnesium, zinc, iron and potassium which makes it suitable for treating tired, sluggish and ageing skin. There are different varieties of clay: *Kaolin (China clay),* used for all skin types, *Fuller's earth,* another variety of kaolin, is used for oily skins and *French green clay,* used for all skin types.

COCOA BUTTER *(Theobroma cacao)*

Cocoa butter is a by product of cocoa pressing. It is obtained from roasted cocoa beans which is the primary ingredient in chocolate or cocoa. As a result, the aroma is of cocoa and the color is yellowish.

Cocoa butter can be applied directly to wrinkles and furrows and does not irritate the skin. It is primarily used as a binder and moisturiser in the production of creams.

Use: 5 - 10%

COCONUT OIL fractionated *(Cocus nucifera)*

To obtain coconut oil, the waxy substance is subjected to heat, which produces the top liquid fraction.

Known as 'water white', coconut oil (fractionated) is a clear, mobile, odorless liquid that penetrates the skin more readily than other carrier oils without leaving an oily, sticky residue. It is the only carrier oil that partially dissolves in water, so it can be used in the bath as it does not leave a greasy tide mark. Fractionated coconut oil has a long shelf life (2 years), without going rancid. Coconut oil, due to its hydrophilic quality, is useful in making **water soluble** cleansing lotions and creams. Coconut oil is used extensively by the cosmetic industry as it gives creams and lotions a smooth consistency. In soap making, coconut oil is used for its lathering and moisturising properties.

Use: Can be used 100%

EVENING PRIMROSE OIL *(Oenothera biennis)*

Evening primrose oil is cold pressed from the seeds and is rich in linoleic acid. A polyunsaturated fatty acid, it contains a small amount of gamma linoleic acid - GLA.

Used externally, evening primrose oil is helpful for eczema, dry, scaly skin and dandruff, and accelerates wound healing. Valuable for skin care, the oil can be used by itself, being one of the few oils that can be used around the eyes. However, it is not for use on an oily skin.

Use: 10% dilution

GRAPESEED OIL *(Vitis vinifera)*

Most Grapeseed oil is produced by hot extraction. The only cold pressed oil to date, of which I am aware of, is produced in France.

Grapeseed oil contains a high percentage of linoleic acid and some Vitamin E. It is a gentle emollient, leaving the skin with a satin finish without feeling greasy.

Use: Can be used 100%.

HAZELNUT OIL *(Corylus avellana)*

Extracted from the Hazelnut tree, it yields an amber yellow oil with a pleasant aroma.

Oleic acid is the principal ingredient with a small proportion of linoleic acid. Hazelnut oil is a very light oil which penetrates the outer layer of the skin easily, making it a superb oil for use around the eyes. It is stimulating to the circulation with astringent *(Great for alleviating puffiness around the eyes.)* properties making the oil beneficial for oily and combination skins. It is also effective on acne.

Use: Can be used 100%.

HEMP SEED OIL *(Cannabis Sativa)*
Hemp seed oil is being called 'Nature's most perfectly balanced oil'. Hemp seed is richer in the essential fatty acids (EFAs) than flax, evening primrose or any other seed oil. Hemp seed contains omega 3 and 6 fatty acids plus gamma linoleic acid (GLA).

HYDROSOLS/HYDROLATS
Rose, Lavender, Orange blossom, and Lemon Balm, when steam distilled, produce hydrosols *(hydrolats)* which are important in skin care due to their rejuvenating abilities. These waters are antiseptic and astringent as well as being skin - soothing. Pure hydrosols are excellent as skin toners. Beware of purchasing hydrosols that are called "floral waters", as these are usually essential oils that have been added to water. A chemical is then added to disperse the essential oil throughout the water.

JOJOBA OIL *(Simmondsia chinensis)*
Jojoba oil is derived from jojoba beans. However, it is technically not an oil but a liquid wax, which, replaced sperm whale oil in the cosmetics industry when the whale became an endangered species. As an added bonus, it is an environmental aid, as planting it saves arid land from becoming desert. The chemical structure not only resembles sebum, but the latter can dissolve in it, which makes it a useful oil in the cases of acne. The fact that it is also indicated for dry skin, psoriasis and eczema shows it to be very balancing, useful for all skin types. One important quality of Jojoba oil is that it becomes firm at temperatures below 50°F. Creams containing Jojoba oil become very firm in the refrigerator. High quality Jojoba oil is without color or odour, making it ideal for cosmetics. Another great quality is that it does not become rancid. Can be used 100%..

KUKUI NUT OIL *(Aleurites moluccana)*

The Kukui nut tree is the official state tree of Hawaii. Within its fruit are the nuts and kernels from which Kukui nut is expressed.

Kukui nut oil is high in linoleic and linolenic acids. It is also easily absorbed by the skin. Research has shown kukui nut oil helps alleviate acne, eczema, psoriasis, sunburns and chapped skin.

Use: 5 - 10%

LANETTE WAX *(INCI name: Cetearyl alcohol and Ceteareth 33)*

Lanette wax is a vegetable derivative of coconut.

Lanette wax binds water and oil together. It serves as an emulsifier base and an emollient in creams and lotions. Be aware that there are 600 lanette waxes on the market, and some of them contain sulphates. Make sure that you get the correct one.

MACADAMIA OIL *Macadamia integrifolia)*

Macadamia oil is oil from the macadamia nut, grown in New South Wales and Queensland. Macadamia oil contains palmitoleic acid, a monounsaturated fatty acid that does not occur in any other plant oil but is found in sebum - especially the sebum of infants, children and teenagers. Palmitoleic acid in sebum diminishes progressively as we get older, therefore, the use of macadamia oil in creams for mature and/or dry skin would be of benefit. Macadamia oil happens also to be hypo allergenic, non-pore clogging while leaving skin smooth and soft. It also provides a protective barrier against moisture loss. Use: Up to 25%

ROSEHIP OIL *(Rosa mosqueta)*

Rosehip oil is derived from the small, oval fruit inside the rose bud.

Research in Chile shows rosehip oil to be a tissue regenerator, which is excellent for a mature skin. It has been shown to be effective on scars, wounds, burns (including sunburn), eczema and ageing.

Use: 10%

SHEA BUTTER *(Butyrospermum parkii)*

Shea butter, also known as African Karite butter, is derived from the pits of the fruit of the African butter tree which grows in central Africa.

Shea butter soothes and softens dry, chapped skin, while nourishing all skin types. For cream and lip balm making, be sure to use naturally refined shea butter or there will be a gritty feeling in the finished product.

Use: *Ideal in cosmetic making* 2 - 5%.

ST. JOHN'S WORT *(Hypericum perforatum)*

The color is a rich reddish ruby hue.

St. John's wort is anti-inflammatory making it useful for wounds, with a soothing action on inflamed nerves, especially on damaged nerve tissue. It is also helpful for burns and bruises.

Use: 2 - 5%

WATER - DISTILLED

Use only pure distilled water when making your creams and lotions. Pure distilled water is free of bacteria and inorganic substances. Tap water contains many unwanted chemical additives.

WHEATGERM OIL *(Triticum vulgare)*

Wheatgerm oil is a yellow/orange color containing many vitamins, particularly vitamin E, as well as carotene and unsaturated fatty acids. Because wheat germ oil is relatively stable; it is sometimes mixed with other oils as it has a high degree of resistance to rancidity. It is helpful for eczema and psoriasis, good for dry and mature skins.

Use: 5 - 10%

WITCH HAZEL *(Hamamelis virginiana)*

Witch hazel is distilled from the leaves, flowers and bark of the hamamelis tree. It has healing, anti-inflammatory and astringent qualities; is particularly helpful as a poultice on bruises and varicose veins.

In skin care it is used in toning lotions and in products for firming the skin. Witch hazel is very effective on oily, acneic skin.

Use: 10%

The Following page contains the
beneficial effects of some fixed and macerated oils

	Avocado	Borage	Calendula	Carrot root	Evening primrose	Hazelnut	Jojoba	Kukui	Macada-mia	Rose-hip	Sesame	St John's wort	Wheatgerm
Acne						X	X	X					
Broken veins			X										
Bruises			X									X	
Burns				X						X		X	
Chapped skin			X					X					
Dry skin	X			X	X		X		X		X		X
Eczema		X	X		X		X	X		X			X
Inflamm-ation			X	X			X					X	
Mature skin				X					X	X			X
Oily skin						X	X						
Psoriasis		X		X	X		X	X					X
Rejuvena-ting		X		X					X	X			X
Scars	X			X						X			
Skin rashes			X									X	
Sunburn	X		X	X				X					
Sun prep.	X			X		X					X		
Varicose veins			X										
Wrinkles	X	X							X	X			

NATURAL PRESERVATIVES and COLOURANTS

The following natural preservatives extend the shelf life of cosmetics by a few months, without altering the other ingredients or causing allergic reactions. They also offer skin-care qualities.

ALKANET

This is extracted from the roots, producing a natural red dye.

BENZOIN RESINOID *(Stryax benzoin)*

Benzoin is a strong natural preservative and a natural fixative. The aroma of Benzoin is pleasant, like vanilla.

See chapter on Essential Oils for further information.

Use: 5-10 drops to 1 litre of cream or lotion.

CARROT ROOT OIL *(Daucus carota)*

As well as being a natural preservative in creams and ointments, carrot oil also makes for a beautiful shade of orange.

GRAPEFRUIT SEED EXTRACT

A by-product of the citrus industry, grapefruit seed extract contains vitamin C and glycerin. It has a seven - nine year shelf life.

Along with its antioxidant properties, grapefruit seed extract is also antibacterial, antimicrobial, deodorizing, astringent and antiseptic.

Use: .05 - .5%

MYRRH *(Commiphora myrrha)*

Because of the antifungal action of Myrrh, it is a good natural preservative.

Use: 5-10 drops to 1 litre of cream or lotion.

TOCOPHEROLS

Tocopherols are naturally derived forms of Vitamin E.

Tocopherols help to delay rancidity in cosmetics. As an added bonus, they offer healing properties, while softening dry skin.

Use: Approximately 5ml to 1 litre of cream or lotion.

Politically Incorrect Ingredients for Natural Cosmetics

AMBERGRIS

This is a wax like substance produced in the intestine of the sperm whale. There is no danger to the whale, but, it is an animal product.

GELATIN

Used for eye gels. The gelatin is obtained from the bone cartilage of animals.

LANOLIN

Lanolin, a purified wax extracted from sheep's wool, easily becomes rancid. It does not penetrate the skin making it useless to use as a carrier for essential oils.

MINERAL OIL

Mineral oil is a petroleum by-product. Although it has a long shelf life, which makes it useful as a commercial item, it does not penetrate the skin making it useless for natural skin care.

PARABENS - *(methyl, ethyl, propyl and benzyl)*

Preservatives used in beauty-care products that make it possible for them to survive the long trip from China and sit on store or warehouse shelves for years. When parabens are applied in a cream, the chemicals appear in the blood within hours. Parabens have been shown to mimic oestrogen, disrupting our bodies' endocrine (hormone) system and have been found in human breast tumours possibly linking them to breast cancer. *For more on preservatives see page 39.*

PETROLEUM JELLY

Petroleum jelly, a mineral fat, does not penetrate the skin, *(see mineral oil page 37).*

SODIUM LAURYL SULPHATE AND SODIUM LAURETH SULPHATE

Makes up to 50% of most shampoos and is found in toothpaste. Originally invented to clean garage floors, SLS has been linked to cataracts and cancer. SLS can actually damage the outer layer of the skin, causing dryness, scaliness, and loss of flexibility. SLS denatures protein and can change genetic material found in cells

SPERMACETI

This hardening agent, used in many face creams, is derived from the whale's head.

Synthetic Preservatives, Colourants, Fragrances & Emulsifiers

Have you ever read the list of ingredients on your skin care products? Believe it or not, many of the ingredients used in your skin, hair and body care products are made actually of industrial strength products and petroleum by-products. This is true for even the most expensive of creams and also products being promoted as "organic and natural".

The following is a small list of some of the chemicals that are being used in cosmetics.

For more information, please refer to "A Consumers Directory of Cosmetic Ingredients", and "The Baby Boomers Beauty Bible".

Boric acid is a dangerous poison used in powdered roach killing products. It is traditionally used to disinfect wounds. It is found in antiseptics, some skin toners and lotions.

Butylated hydroxytoluene (BHT) A paraben/synthetic preservative, known to be toxic, can cause allergic reactions and skin rashes. It may-be associated with breast cancer.

Dehydroacetic acid (DHA) Used as a preservative in cosmetics. Although not irritating to the skin, it can cause kidney damage if ingested.

FD & C colours are derived from the coal tar used to make synthetic dyes.

Fragrances (synthetic) as opposed to aromatic essential oils are one of the worst culprits for allergic reactions and highly toxic to the body. Synthetic fragrances contain multiple chemical compounds; anywhere from 10 to several hundred. Phthalates, which are plasticizers, are commonly used in the manufacture of plastics. They are used in fragrance formulations. So beware of any product that contains *"perfume or fragrance"*.

Germall plus, INCI name: Diazolidinyl Urea, Iodopropynyl Butylcarbamate and Propylene Glycol *(anti-freeze).*

Hydroquinone is used in skin lightening creams. The FDA proposed a ban in 2006 as it is thought to be carcinogenic and it causes a condition of the skin, where after regular use, causes a thickening and darkening of the skin.

Hydantoin (DMDM) is a preservative that releases formaldehyde that is used in embalming.

Parabens *See page 38*

Phenoxyethanol known as ethylene glycol phenyl ether or ethylene glycol monophenyl ether is a derived from natural sources and, is known to cause DNA mutations, is an endocrine disrupter and can damage the bladder. This was found when tested on animals. It has not been tested on humans. It is even allowed by the organic soil association in the UK, so most natural shampoos contain 1 tsp. to 200ml bottle of shampoo.

If in doubt, do not use. Remember, it is your skin!!!

PART TWO
The Creamy Craft
of
Cosmetic Making.

Most creams and lotions are preparations that form a protective film holding in the skin's moisture and clogging the pores, which do not allow for moisture and healthy substances to penetrate the skin.

These preparations usually contain one or more of the following ingredients: mineral oil, petroleum jelly, petroleum by-products, parabens, sulphates and lanolin. *(See pages 37 through to 40 for more information).*

However, the following creams and lotions are unique as they do not contain any of the above ingredients. The creams and lotions are made up entirely of vegetable oils, which to a certain degree penetrate the outer layer of the skin to the dermis. They, not only benefit the skin, but contain politically correct ingredients. Vegetable oils carry the essential oils through the skin into the body, via the blood stream affecting all the internal systems of the body i.e. circulatory, cardio vascular and lymphatic systems, digestive, endocrine, nervous, urinary, and bone and muscular systems. The proper terms for these creams and lotions are ***carrier creams*** *and* ***carrier lotions.***

The basic white cream and white lotion from the following recipes can be adapted for many skin types with more or less water; other vegetable oils can also be added or substituted. Be creative; I have left a couple of pages at the back of this book to allow for your personal cream making history. When you try the recipes in this book, keep a record of how they worked for you. Experiment with ingredient changes and note as well.

My other book 'the baby boomer's beauty bible' 2004, shows my own personal growth in cream making with many new recipes and treatments for specific skin conditions.

The following recipes teach you how to make the base creams, lotions and ointments. I have included a few variations to get you into your creative mode. All these creams and lotions are, by themselves, excellent as treatments for oily, acne, dry, or mature skin, depending on the oils being used. To improve on the therapeutic quality of the creams, I have added some recipes, with which you can add essential oils to your favorite base cream or lotion.

These recipes are simple and contain lots of skin - friendly ingredients.

TOOLS OF THE TRADE

Do you remember the scene in Jack Lemmon's movie *The Apartment* when he tried straining cooked spaghetti through an old tennis racquet? Of course, it wasn't surprising that the meal turned into a disaster in more ways than one, because cookery and cream making is like anything else, you must use the proper tools for the job.

You will need the following equipment:

- 1 double boiler (or a glass bowl to be placed over a pot of boiling water
- 1 Stainless steel saucepan.
- A wooden spoon.
- Spoons for measuring.
- A measuring jug 1 litre.
- A small measuring cup 1 to 30ml.
- A scale that will measure grams.
- Empty glass jars for creams, dark (amber coloured) bottles for toners, body and facial oils.
- Labels and a waterproof felt-tip pen.

Clean all equipment in boiling water or at least wash them well with hot soapy water; rinse well and dry. It is best to use these utensils only for making cosmetics and not to prepare or store food in them.

Cautions

- Pay attention when heating oil:
- If the phone or doorbell goes, remove pan from heat. Small amounts of oils like this can overheat in seconds if left unattended.
- Do not overheat the oils.
- Keep young children and pets out of the way.
- Keep a bottle of Lavender nearby in the event of being burnt by oil.
- Immediately remove any oil or cream split on the floor.

Basic white lotion

Ingredients

Lanette wax 30g
Fractionated coconut oil 50ml
Rose hydrosol100ml
Distilled water 600ml
Grapefruit seed extract 2ml

Method

1. Sterilize all utensils and worktop.
2. Melt the lanette wax and coconut oil in a heat resistant bowl over boiling water (or in a double boiler).
3. Put the water and Rose hydrosol into the other saucepan. Heat gently.
4. Stir the wax and oils until they have completely melted.
5. Heat water until it has almost reached boiling point. Then remove from heat.
6. Slowly, start to add water from the saucepan to the melted wax and oils, stirring constantly, until all water has been added.
7. Remove the heat resistant bowl from pan of boiling water and place on a heat resistant pad.
8. Continue stirring until the mixture has completely cooled.
9. When the mixture has cooled sufficiently, add the grapefruit seed extract.
10. Pour whilst still warm lotion into sterilized bottles.

Variation: Rich white lotion

To the lanette wax, add 5ml of shea butter and/or 10ml of macadamia nut oil. If your skin is particularly dry, then you can add 5ml of carrot root and 10ml of avocado oils and a dollop of vitamin E.

Basic white cream

Ingredients:

Lanette wax 30g

Shea butter 5ml

Sweet almond oil 40ml

Fractionated coconut oil 20ml

Rose hydrosol 50ml

Distilled water 300ml

Vitamin E 1 dollop

Grapefruit seed extract 2ml

Myrrh essential oil 5 drops

Method:

Melt the lanette wax, almond and coconut oils in a double boiler. Heat the rose hydrosol and distilled water in the other pan. When the wax and oils have completely melted, **slowly** add the heated (not boiling) water to the fats, stirring all the time. Remove the heat resistant bowl, containing the fats and water, from the heat. Continue stirring until the mixture has completely cooled. Add the vitamin E, grapefruit seed extract and essential oil of myrrh. Put into sterilized jars.

Variations:

Carrot cream

Skin type: Normal/dry

Ingredients:

Lanette wax 60g
Shea butter 5 ml
Almond oil 70ml
Macadamia oil 10ml
Avocado oil 30ml
Hemp seed oil 10ml
Carrot root oil 3ml
Orange flower hydrosol 50ml
Distilled water 500ml
Vitamin E 1ml
Grapefruit seed extract 2ml
Myrrh essential oil 5 drops
Benzoin resinoid 1 dollop

Method:

Melt the lanette wax, shea butter and oils in the double boiler. Heat the orange flower and distilled waters in the other pan. When heated to approximately to the same temperature, slowly add the water to the melted wax and oil. Continue stirring until the mixture has cooled; then add the vitamin E, grapefruit seed extract, benzoin and myrrh

Hazelnut cream

Skin type: Normal/oily

(This cream is especially suited for the skin around the eyes).

Ingredients:

Lanette wax 30g

Hazelnut oil 30ml

Rose or Lemon balm hydrosol 50ml

Witch hazel 20ml (optional)

Distilled water 350ml

Vitamin E 2ml

Grapefruit seed extract 3ml

Follow method as for the carrot cream.

Jojoba cream

Another recipe suitable for all skin types, especially for oily/acne.

Replace the hazelnut oil with the Jojoba. You can keep the rose hydrosol if you wish, or replace the rose hydrosol with another hydrosol of your choice.

Make exactly the same way as for the basic white cream.

Allergy cream

For people who have eczema, hay fever or asthma in the family history.

Make as for the basic white cream; replace the coconut oil with borage 20ml, and replace 20ml of the almond oil with Kukui oil. Omit the shea butter.

Total amount of carrier oil used should add up to 60ml.

Calendula cream

Chapped/dry skin

Again as for basic white cream, replace the coconut oil for calendula. Use up to 50ml less distilled water to make the cream a little thicker.

Basic Ointment

This is useful as an ointment for protecting the skin. This recipe works well on chronic psoriasis and is a good healing base for sores, cuts, rashes etc.

Ingredients:

Bees wax 15g

Shea butter 5ml or cocoa butter 5ml

Almond oil 50ml

Coconut oil 20ml

Avocado oil 10ml

Macadamia oil 10ml

Wheatgerm oil 10ml

Myrrh essential oil 5 drops

Benzoin resinoid 1 dollop

Method:

Melt the bees wax in a double boiler. When it is almost melted, add the butter.

Slowly add the oils, stirring all the time.

When the wax and oils are completely melted, remove from the heat. Add the essential oils plus any additional essential oils that you may want to include such as Tea tree, Lavender etc. *(Maximum 30 drops).*

Immediately pour into sterilized jars while still liquid

PART THREE

Skin School and Recipes

The skin is an organ and the outer covering of the body. It has the following parts:

The outer layer called the epidermis contains nerve endings but no blood vessels. It is nourished by the tissue fluid derived from the dermis.

The inner layer called the dermis, contains the sebaceous glands which secrete sebum, sudoriferous glands (known as sweat glands) which extract water, salts, urea and other waste products, and discharges them onto the skin as sweat. The dermis also contains sensory nerve endings, and blood and lymphatic vessels.

Functions of the skin

- Forms a protective covering for the body.
- Contains the end organs of the sensory nerves (pain, touch and temperature).
- Secretes sebum.
- Capable of absorbing small amounts of oily substances.
- Gives origin to the hair and nails.
- Contains dehydrocholesterol which is converted into vitamin D by the action of sunlight.
- Secretes sweat and by doing so it a, acts as an excretory organ by removing waste products i.e. salt and water and b, helps regulate body temperature.
- 8. Drugs can be absorbed through the skin.

SKIN TYPES

Normal skin

Normal skin is much rarer than one would imagine, especially in industrial areas. The skin is smooth, healthy, fine-pored with a fairly thick epidermis; it is evenly supplied with oil and moisture and if looked after and not abused, remains smooth and unwrinkled to a fairly late age.

Dry skin

Dry skin is characterized by a lack of fat or moisture caused by insufficient flow of sebum from the sebaceous glands. The epidermis is thin, the complexion pink and the surface frequently scaly. Dry skin wrinkles easily, often prematurely.

Sensitive skin

Sensitive skin is characterized by the appearance of broken red capillaries usually found on the cheeks and nose. This type of skin is fair and delicate usually found on redheads. Sensitive skin reacts strongly to the sun, stress, and many synthetic substances in cosmetics.

Oily skin

Oily skin, caused by the over activity of the sebaceous glands, is usually very thick and is often coarse in texture, moist in appearance, open-pored usually accompanied by pimples and blackheads; it is frequently sallow and dead looking.

Combination skin

This is a mixture of dry and oily skin; it is characterized by a wide greasy panel running down from the forehead and nose to the chin whilst the rest of the skin is dry.

Common disorders of the skin

Acne vulgaris known as common acne

Acne is a disorder of the sebaceous glands common in adolescence, associated with the increase of sex hormones at puberty in both male and female. When there is an imbalance of hormones, the sebaceous gland in the skin increases in size and secretes extra sebum. This excess oil is the root of the trouble. The sebum makes the skin surface oily which interferes with the pH balance of the skin encouraging the growth of bacteria. It also tends to prevent the outer layer from shedding which blocks and plugs the oil glands. The oil then becomes trapped within the ducts leading from the sebaceous gland to the surface of the skin where it mixes with accumulated dead skin cells and bacteria to form a plug or blackhead (comedo). The resulting blackness is not necessarily dirt as is commonly thought. It is the result of a chemical change in the mixture of cell bacteria and oily secretions. When the sebum has no way of leaving the skin, it stays below the skin surface causing inflammation which appears as a red raised lump (pimple) that may be infected. To fight the infection, the white blood cells enter the area and destroy the invading bacteria. Dead bacteria and dead white blood cells form what is known as pus.

Acne Rosacea

This is not related to common acne but is a chronic inflammatory condition which affects the nose and cheeks. It occurs most frequently in middle-aged women in whom it is associated with intestinal disturbances or pelvic disease.

Age spots

This is also known as liver spots or brown spots under the medical name *lentigos.* These marks are caused by changes in pigmentation in areas of the skin that have been exposed to the sun and are promoted by ultraviolet radiation and contact with perfumes or eau de colognes.

Eczema

Eczema is an acute or chronic inflammation of the skin showing scales or crusts. Not infectious, it itches and burns and there is the exudation of lymph due to hypersensitive skin. Usually the tendency to eczema is inherited.

Psoriasis

Psoriasis is a chronic inflammatory disease estimated to affect some 3 to 5% of the population. It somewhat resembles eczema. It is recognized by elevated reddish patches covered by thick, dry, scaly patches of silver coloured scabs. When these scales are lifted, tiny bleeding points may be noticed. Its cause is unknown; food and nerves may be partially responsible.

Seborrhea

Seborrhea is due to over activity and excessive secretion of sebaceous or oil glands. The appearance is oily and shiny.

Thread veins

These are also known as split veins and broken veins. Due to weakness in the fine blood vessels and through congestion in the dilation of the capillaries, very tiny blood vessels appear resulting in a fine mess red blotches or florid patches. The cheeks appear to have a permanent blush; sensitive skins frequently suffer from the problem. It can be caused by alcohol, caffeine, exposure to extreme hot or cold conditions and hot spicy foods. Thread veins on the legs may be caused by standing for long periods or by wearing too tight clothing restricting the circulation.

Recipes

CLEANSERS

All vegetable and nut oils can be used for cleansing the skin as well as for nourishing the skin. My particular favourite is fractionated coconut oil because of its water soluble property.

Cleansing Lotion

The following cleansing lotion deeply cleanses skin, removing all traces of grime and makeup. Use daily, wiping off excess with damp cotton wool and follow with a skin toner and moisturiser. This is suitable for all skin types.

Ingredients

Lanette wax 30g

Fractionated coconut oil 40ml

Rose hydrosol 100ml

Distilled water 600ml

Grapefruit seed extract 2ml

Geranium essential oil 10 - 20 drops

Lavender essential oil 10 - 20 drops

Method

Make exactly the same as for basic white lotion. Add the essential oils when the mixture has completely cooled.

Variation:

For a **richer cleansing cream** use less distilled water (400ml instead of 600ml) and add 20ml sweet almond oil.

Facial scrub

To be used after cleansing on all skins except sensitive, twice a week.

Ingredients

2 tbs. dry Rose petals
2 tbs. Lavender flowers
1 Chamomile tea bag
1 tsp. Ground walnut shells
3 drops Lavender essential oil
2 drops Clary sage essential oil
1 drop Neroli essential oil
3 drops Chamomile essential oil
15g Honey

Method

1. Grind the rose petals to smaller flakes
2. Add essential oils to the walnut meal and mix.
3. Add nut meal and lavender flowers to the grinder mix with rose petals until mixture resembles an even, fine meal.
4. Add contents of chamomile into rest of mix.
5. Prepare 15gm of the mix, add 15gm of honey; let it sit for a few hours.
6. Apply on the face with gentle circular, upward strokes. Rinse off with water.

TONERS:

Toners rinse away traces of oils and fats (residue from the cleansers); they help to close the pores, restore the skin's acid mantle (the pH factor), stimulate circulation and refine texture.

Tone after cleansing and follow with a moisturiser.

Basic skin toner

Ingredients:

Rose hydrosol 90ml
Witch hazel 10ml
Geranium essential oil 5 drops
Lavender essential oil 5 drops

Method:

Simply combine and bottle.

Note: For a witch hazel toner, simply increase the ratio of witch hazel from 10% to 30% to rose hydrosol 70ml. Rose hydrosol can be substituted for orange flower, chamomile, lavender or lemon balm hydrosols.

Morning mist toning lotion

Ingredients:

Distilled water 95ml
Pure alcohol 3ml *(vodka will do)*
Lemon essential oil 5 drops
Rosemary essential oil 5 drops
Rose absolute 1 drop

Method:

1. Pour alcohol into a spray pump bottle; then add the essential oils of rose, lemon and rosemary. Then shake.

2. Add distilled water to the blend.

Note: Alcohol evaporates, and if sprayed, will not affect the skin.

MOISTURE CREAMS AND LOTIONS

Moisturisers protect and nourish the skin. The wind, sun and central heating dry out our skin leaving the skin dryer than it should be. Moisturisers replace the loss of moisture in the skin, even people with oily skins need a moisturiser to replace the moisture loss. These moisturisers are specifically designed to carry the essential oils into the skin so that the essential oils can work their magic.

Moisturise when the skin is moist, after cleansing and toning.

Choose 30ml of carrier cream or lotion of your choice, depending on your skin type and your skin needs at that moment in time, and add 6 - 15 drops of essential oil/s.

The following recipes will help you in determining the appropriate solution.

FACIAL OILS

Carrier oils by themselves make excellent moisturisers and are especially useful for night treatments, one of my favourite being jojoba; it is good for all skin types. Just replace the base cream with any one of the following carrier oils: hazelnut, sweet almond, or jojoba with or without 10% of one of the following oils, borage, wheatgerm, macadamia, avocado, St. Johns wort, kukui and calendula.

If you do use any oils other than jojoba, then add a dollop of vitamin E to help prevent rancidity.

Follow as with the moisturisers; 8 - 15 drops of essential oil/s to 30ml of carrier oil.

Moisture cream Normal/oily

This cream is particularly helpful in reducing the sebum production in the skin.

To 30ml of the Jojoba or Hazelnut base cream, add the following essential oils:

Juniper berry 4 drops

Geranium 6 drops

Lavender 5 drops

Moisture cream Oily/acne

To 30ml of the Jojoba or Hazelnut base cream, add the following essential oils:

Lemongrass 3 drops

Cedarwood 3 drops

Juniper berry 5 drops

Moisture cream Sensitive

This cream is particularly helpful for sensitive, irritated skin and after sun care.

To 30ml of carrot cream base, add the following essential oils.

Roman chamomile 4 drops

Ho wood/leaf 2 drops

Lavender 2 drops

Rose 1 drop

Moisture cream Normal/dry

To 30ml of the carrot cream base, add the following essential oils:

Sandalwood 3 drops

Geranium 3 drops

Ho leaf/wood 2 drops

Ylang Ylang 1 drop

Super firming Eye Cream

This formula will soothe as it tightens the skin around the eyes.

Apply after cleansing and toning. Using ring finger only, take a small amount of the eye cream and circle around eyes from temple to nose on eyelid and circle up back and out to temple on upper lid. Continue circling.

To 30ml of the Hazelnut cream, add 1 drop each of cypress, German chamomile and Roman chamomile essential oils.

NIGHT TREATMENTS:

For special treatments, use the following creams at night. After cleansing and toning, gently massage a thin film of the night cream or wrinkle attack cream into the skin, using the fingertips in upward and outwards strokes over the jaw and throat areas and in semi - circular movements around the eyes *(very gently here)*. Leave on overnight

Night cream

To 30ml of the base cream of your choice, depending on your skin type, add the following essential oils:

Frankincense 6 drops

Lavender 6 drops

Neroli 2 drops

Rose 1 drop

Neck firming cream

To the 30ml of the Hazelnut cream, add the following essential oils:

Cypress 5 drops

Lemon 4 drops

Fennel 3 drops

Frankincense 3 drops

Wrinkle attack cream

To 30ml of the cream of your choice, add the following essential oils:

Clary sage 3 drops
Frankincense or Carrot seed 3 drops
Lavender 3 drops

Bergamot 2 drops
Neroli 1 drop

Treatments including, fruit acids and face masks.

All types of skin can benefit from using face masks as they help to remove the dead surface cells. If these are not taken away, the skin becomes flaky or rough. In addition, the dead cells clog up the pores and prevent normal skin activity.

Fruit acid lotion

Fruit acids gently exfoliate and smooth the skin. There is also some evidence that they stimulate skin repair. Most mainstream commercial companies now have products containing fruit acids.

This is the aromatherapy alternative.

To 15ml of the basic white lotion, add the following essential oils.

Grapefruit essential oil 6 drops

Lemon essential oil 6 drops

Bergamot essential oil 6 drops

This is to be used after cleansing and toning and 10 minutes before moisturising. Use twice daily; some tingling might be felt due to the working action on the skin.

Caution: Do not use close to the eyes and not before sunbathing.

Treatment masks

Put on to the skin in upward and outward movements avoiding the area around the eyes. Cover the eyes with witch hazel pads or cotton wool soaked with pure cucumber juice. Leave on until the mask is dry, approximately 10 minutes. Remove and follow with a toner and then moisturise with a treatment cream. Use up to twice a week.

Normal skin

1 tbs. of white clay Kaolin (china clay)

1 tsp. honey

2 drops of Geranium essential oil

Add Rose hydrosol to make a paste.

Dry skin

1 tbs. of French green clay

1 tsp. honey

1 drop of Lavender essential oil

1 drop of Ho leaf/wood essential oil

Add Neroli hydrosol to make a paste

Oily skin

1 tbs.. of Fuller's earth

1 ½ tsp.. Jojoba oil

1 drop of Lavender essential oil

1 drop of Lemon essential oil

Add Witch hazel to make a paste.

Sensitive skin

2 tbs. Kaolin

1 tsp. honey

1 drop Roman Chamomile essential oil

1 drop of Lavender essential oil

Add Rose hydrosol to make a paste.

SPECIAL RECIPES

Eczema cream

To 30ml of the Allergy cream, add the following essential oils:

Bergamot 5 drops

Geranium 5 drops

Juniper berry 5 drops

Lavender 5 drops

Scar care cream

To 25ml of the carrot cream, add 5ml of Rosehip oil and the following essential oils:

Frankincense 5 drops

Myrrh 3 drops

Lavender 5 drops

Acne

I have dealt with many teenagers over the years that have acne and spotty skins. I know that it can be a nightmare for those that suffer acne.

The worst thing one can do to solve this problem is to use astringents and products with alcohol as this desiccates the skin causing more oil to be produced. You, the victim, are caught in a vicious circle.

You must be gentle with your skin. Don't squeeze your zits. A good Zit Zapper is a drop of essential oil of Lavender applied directly to the spot and left overnight. Results guaranteed!

With regard to skin care, first, cleanse your facial skin twice a day with a mild soap *(like the cleansing cake made from pure olive oil, available at the Aroma shoppe),* or a natural cleansing lotion. Follow the cleansing with a mild tonic lotion to balance the pH factor of the skin. At this time, moisturiser can be used, but make sure it is very light, containing neither lanolin or mineral oils as they can clog the pores of the skin.

For more information and skin treatments for acne, sensitive skin and ageing skin, please refer to the "Baby Boomers beauty Bible".

An ideal home moisturiser can be made from the following recipe:

6 drops of essential oil of Geranium,
6 drops of essential oil of Rosemary,
4 drops of essential oil of Lavender
in a base of Jojoba oil 50ml.

Jojoba is excellent for acne as it dissolves sebum, the cause of blackheads.

Use both day and night.

In addition to the use of a moisturiser, a good clay mask used once a week draws out impurities.

Aside from external care, the skin responds to a good diet containing lots of vegetables, fruits, plain yogurt, whole grains, seeds (pumpkin, sesame and sunflower) and water. Obviously avoid or at least reduce the consumption of the traditional villains such as hamburgers, chips, soft drinks, candies and cookies. Our heroes, used in moderation, are vitamins A and B, zinc and selenium.

Lime lip balm

In addition to preventing and healing cracked, dry lips, this lip balm will also prevent the development of cold sores.

Ingredients

Beeswax 15g

Shea butter 5g

Almond oil 40ml

Macadamia nut oil 10ml

Avocado oil 10ml

Coconut oil 10ml

Hemp seed oil 20ml

Vitamin E oil 10ml

Lime essential oil 25 drops

Myrrh essential oil 5 drops

Benzoin 1 dollop

Optional; You can add up to 5ml of Alkanet root oil for a pink/red gloss or 5ml of Carrot oil for an orange gloss.

Method

Make exactly the same way as the basic ointment. Jar immediately.

For those of you who would like to make healthy natural lipsticks using pure and natural pigments, please read *"The Little Book of Lipsticks" 2010.*

Suggested skin care routine

A skin treatment schedule (see below) is important in maintaining good skin. Cleansing, toning and moisturising should be done twice a day. Exfoliation and facial treatments are useful for best results, ideally once a week.

SKIN TREATMENT SCHEDULE

	Sensitive	Oily	Ageing	Dry
Cleanse *twice daily (morning and evening)*	Cleansing lotion	Cleansing lotion	Cleansing lotion	Rich cleansing cream
Scrub *twice weekly*	Scrub when needed but not on sensitive skin			
Tone *twice daily after cleansing*	Skin toner, Neroli or Chamomile	Witch hazel toner or Morning mist	Skin toner or Morning mist	Skin toner, Neroli or Rose hydrosol.
Moisturise *twice daily*	Use the appropriate moisturiser for skin type			
Specialized *once a day*	Eye cream	Eye cream	Wrinkle attack, Eye cream & Neck firming.	Superlight eye cream
Fruit Acid Lotion *to be used after toning*	Use when needed but not on sensitive skin.			
Mask *once a week*	Use the appropriate mask for skin type.			

A 10 Step Guide Towards a Healthy, Younger Skin

We cannot stop ageing, but by following a few basic steps, the skin on the face, whether it be dry, prematurely wrinkled, congested, grey or sallow looking , can be helped at any age.

This guide of do's and don'ts can also be used as a preventative measure.

1. **WATER** To eliminate dryness. Drink 6-8 glasses daily. Water is a natural cleansing agent in the body. With constant use, toxins and waste products in the colon are flushed out and, as a result, the skin becomes clear of congestion.

2. **NUTRITION** Eat plenty of fruits and vegetables which are high in nutrients beneficial to the skin. Specifically, take, in moderation Vitamin A, C and Zinc which are known to be good for the skin. Follow the acid/alkaline balanced diet in the cellulite and fat treatment chapter.

3. **COFFEE** Cut out coffee and see for yourself the skins improvement. Coffee depletes vital minerals and nutrients from the body; hence, the skin suffers.

4. **ALCOHOL** Excessive use of alcohol, like coffee, robs the body of nutrients thereby, contributing to ageing of the skin.

5. **SMOKING** A big NO NO!
   Look at the skin of any heavy smoker (Point made!)

6. **EXERCISE** Regular exercise e.g. 1 hour, 3 times a week of brisk walking or Martial Arts *(A side benefit, learn self-defense).* Exercise will oxygenate the skin, thereby giving it a nice glow dissipating the grey, lifeless look, not in fashion at the moment. An excellent specific exercise to firm the skin around the neck is to gently arch the head back and then try to touch the tip of your nose with the tip of your tongue (ten times daily); this is better done at home rather than in the subway to reduce comments by the public.

7. **EXFOLIATE** by using fruit acids, facial scrubs and treatment masks.
   To help reduce fine lines and age spots.

8. **SUN** Sunlight is good, but too much sun damages and thickens the skin causing premature aging. Try to avoid heavy exposure to the sun.

9. **THINK POSITIVELY** Stress and tension show up on your face as frown lines etc. Take some time for yourself. Have a Massage. Take Relaxation therapy classes. Take some time to breathe and smell the flowers.

10. **SKIN CARE** Be gentle with your skin. Cleanse with a gentle cleansing lotion. Follow with an alcohol free toning lotion to balance the pH factor of the skin. Moisturise with a good quality cream. My favourite moistursers for **anti-ageing** can be found in the moisturising section of this book specifically the **wrinkle attack** cream and the **neck firming** cream.

Additional recipes including ***Rejuvenating and firming treatments*** *can be found in 'the Baby Boomers Beauty Bible'.*

PART FOUR
Body Care

As with the care of the face, the skin on the body needs exfoliating and nourishing.

One way of exfoliating is to skin brush twice a day. This is done dry before bathing in the direction of the lymphatic system.

Other ways are through using body scrubs and taking regular salt baths.

BASIC RECIPE FOR SALT BATH

Add up to 30 drops of essential oil/s to 150g of sea salts or a mixture *(see below),* in a glass container with lid. Shake well and age one week.

For a single treatment, add up to 10 drops to 50 grams of sea salt.

VARIATION

Ingredients

50g Epsom salts
75g Sea salt
15g Baking soda
10g citric acid

Optional: Add 15g of fresh herbs or flowers (leave whole with woody parts removed).

This bath salt mix with the citric acid will have a champagne effect in the bath, similar to using bath bomb

Method:

Blend the salts, citric acid and baking soda in a food processor. Stir in 30 drops of essential oil/s then add the whole flowers or herbs.

The essential oils can make a difference to how you want to feel. You can use the toxin eliminator bath mix to detoxifying your body, or make an exotic bath by adding one of the exotic blends to the salt bath for a relaxing and sensuous bath.

For a fresh fruity uplifting bath, use the following essential oils to 50 grams of the salt bath mix.

3 drops Petitgrain
3 drops Lemon
3 drops Bergamot

After the bath, use a body lotion or oil for a smooth, soft skin.

Body lotion or oil

For a body lotion, use either the basic white lotion or the rich white lotion for a dryer skin. Add to 50ml of either lotion or oil (almond or jojoba) 15 to 30 drops of your favourite blend of essential oils. If you prefer to use oil, make sure that it is pure, cold pressed, see the chapter *Politically correct ingredients.*

Try some of the following recipes and use when needed.

Add one of the following essential oil blends
to 50ml basic white lotion or oil

Anti-stress

Clary sage 15 drops

Lemon 10 drops

Lavender 5 drops

Pre-exercise

Grapefruit 8 drops

Cypress 6 drops

Geranium 3 drops

Poor circulation

Benzoin 8 drops

Black pepper 12 drops

Juniper berry 10 drops

Varicose veins

Lemon 10 drops

Cypress 15 drops

Peppermint 5 drops

Aches and pains

Eucalyptus 8 drops

Rosemary 8 drops

Sage 12 drops

An alternative to using oils or lotions on the body would be to use dusting powder.

My favourite is to use arrowroot as a base but cornstarch or rice powder can also be used.

BASIC RECIPE FOR DUSTING POWDER

Choose the base powder of your choice and mix 15 drops of your favourite essential oil blend with one cup base powder in a food processor.

VARIATION

Blend 100gm's powdered lavender flowers, 25gm's powdered rose petals, 100gm's rice powder and 100gm's arrowroot in a food processor. Add a few drops of lavender essential oil and blend again.

To add a little pinky sparkle to your skin, add a little powdered **lepidolite** to your dusting powder. This crystal is used for stress reduction; it contains natural *lithium* which is an antidepressant. Of special note, lepidolite provides smoothness to the skin *(useful for wrinkles)* and on energy level helps to gently induce change allowing for a smooth passage.

Cellulite and Fat Treatment

Here are some healthy hints and fast facts…

We are always looking for the magic formulae to reduce fat and cellulite. I can assure you that if you follow this game plan there will be a slimmer and healthier you.

1. Drink plenty of water 6 - 8 250ml glasses a day.
2. Follow the acid /alkaline balanced diet.
3. Drink detoxifying tea. One cup, three times a day
4. Exercise at least three times a week.
5. Skin brush twice daily.
6. This is done dry before bathing. Using real bristles, brush in upward movements all over the body following the lymphatic circulation *(brush down on the abdomen).* Avoid face, neck and breasts.
7. Take daily toxin eliminator baths in the evening, Scrub with detoxifying body scrub during the bath.
8. Twice a day, once after the toxin eliminator bath, massage with either the cellulite lotion/oil or fat buster lotion/oil
9. Last, but not least, in the morning look at yourself in the mirror eye to eye and say "I am beautiful, healthy and getting slimmer everyday". Say this nine times.

Detoxifying tea

Alfalfa leaf 15g

Coltsfoot 30g

Dandelion root 15g

Stinging nettle 30g

Oat straw 30m

Raspberry leaves 30g

To each heaping teaspoon of the above mixture add 1 cup of boiling water. Steep 10-15 minutes, strain; drink 3 cups daily.

Detoxifying body scrub

Rice, arrowroot powder or Corn starch 100g

Walnut shells (ground) 100g

Fennel essential oil 5 drops

Grapefruit essential oil 10 drops

Juniper berry essential oil 5 drops

Sage essential oil 5 drops

Mix and leave for at least a week. After taking the toxin eliminator bath, stand up in the bath and take a small handful of the blend and rub in circular motions into the cellulite for at least 10 minutes. Then, rinse off with a warm then cold shower. Follow with either cellulite or fat buster massage lotion or oil.

Toxin Eliminator bath

Add 10 drops of essential oils to 30 grams of the following; which can be a blend of micronized marine algae, sea and Epsom salts. Age 1 week and use the entire amount per bath.

Sage 2 drops

Juniper berry 2 drops

Lemon 3 drops

Grapefruit 3 drops

Cellulite Attack lotion/oil

To 50ml of the base white lotion or grapeseed 40ml and jojoba oil 10ml, add the following essential oils:

Fennel 10 drops

Grapefruit 12 drops

Cypress 8 drops

Fat Buster lotion/oil

To 50ml of the base white lotion or grapeseed oil, add the following essential oils:

Lime 10 drops

Juniper berry 5 drops

Basil 10 drops

Petitgrain 5 drops

Acid and Alkaline balanced diet.

Beauty begins inside. Toxins in the blood, poor digestion or a sluggish colon are prime suspects if you have bad cellulite. If you want to have a lean body with beautiful clear skin, **change to an alkaline diet** with plenty of raw vegetables and fruit. Cut out sugar, chocolate, white flour and most foods from packets and jars. Since you are beginning from inside the body, an important internal fact is the chemical makeup, 80% alkaline and 20% acid. However, in direct opposition to this state people tend to eat 80% acid-forming foods and 20% alkaline-forming foods. Notice that I mention **alkaline-forming.** Foods such as lemon and apple cider vinegar are not acid-forming but alkaline-forming in the body. A general rule is that approximately 3/4 of your plate should be alkaline and 1/4 acid. if one meal is completely acid, i.e., a cheese sandwich and coffee, you must not panic. Balance the body and make sure that the next two meals are 100% alkaline forming.

To assist in your quest to go alkaline here are some helpful hints:

ALKALINE FORMING FOODS

VEGETABLES: All vegetables, including potatoes, except brussel sprouts, are alkaline forming. Eat both raw and steamed, the potatoes baked in their skins. Try to have two large vegetable salads a day.

FRUIT: Fresh fruits are cleansing. They should be eaten, one type of fruit at a time, not mixed. Eat fruits in the morning or at least two hours after a meal.

FATS AND OILS: Use only cold pressed oils. Sunflower, safflower, and olive oils are vital to the body. Unfortunately, oils found in the supermarkets are generally not cold pressed.

SEEDS AND NUTS: Sunflower, sesame and pumpkin seeds together form a complete protein. Add the three seeds to natural, plain yogurt and the meal is complete. In regard to nuts, **almonds are the only nuts that are alkaline-forming.** They may be also added to yogurt or eaten as a snack.

YOGURT: Use plain, natural only. The culture in the yogurt helps to balance the flora and the good bacteria in the colon. The only fruit that you can add to yogurt is bananas. Fruit destroys the culture in the yogurt, as do sugar, maple syrup and honey.

SUGAR: Use both unpasteurized honey and maple syrup as they are the only ones which are alkaline-forming.

DRINKS: Water, fresh juices, herb teas and dandelion coffee are good cleansing alkaline drinks.

Now, don't get carried away and eliminate all acid-forming foods. Maintain the proper balance of 20%.

ACID-FORMING FOODS:

GRAINS AND CEREALS: Gluten found in wheat, rye and oats can cause intestinal difficulties. Avoid pastries, biscuits, white flour, pasta and white rice. Eat within 20%, whole grain breads, such as spelt or rye bread, whole grain pastas such as buckwheat, spelt and whole grain rice.

PROTEIN: Although acid-forming, I do recommend having some meat, chicken or fish daily and offal twice weekly. It is important that it is of high quality, i.e. Grain - fed chicken as opposed to factory fed chickens.

DAIRY PRODUCTS: Cheese and milk, in addition to being acid-forming, are also mucous forming, so keep their consumption a minimum. Eggs should be used in moderation, no more often than four times a week. Use butter in moderation.

DRINKS: Sugary soft drinks, coffee, decaffeinated coffee, tea and alcohol are all acid-forming.

AVOID: Salt, white sugar, processed foods. white flour, fried foods and anything in excess.

After the Diet

Hopefully, if you are reading this, then you have succeeded in your quest of losing the excess weight and cellulite. Now we have to deal with another problem, stretch marks and loose skin.

Here is a five-point plan of action.

1. **Exercise,** the abdomen to tone the muscle. A good example is SCRUNCHES: Lie on your back with knees bent, soles of feet on the floor and fingers at temple with elbows out. Now lift shoulders and head six inches from the floor. Hold for a count of five then slowly lower your shoulders. Repeat twenty times a day. Aside from this sort of specific exercise, it would be a good idea to take a general exercise class, such as swimming, yoga or martial arts. Any one of these will improve your general vitality and health.

2. **Skin brush**. To increase blood circulation and lymphatic drainage.

3. **Massage** every day with the following essential oil mixture.

Anti-stretch Mark lotion/oil

To 45ml of either Almond oil or basic white lotion, add

Rosehip 5ml
Lavender 15 drops
Frankincense 10 drops
Lemongrass 5 drops

Shake well, apply twice daily. Stretch marks will improve over time, but do not expect deep stretch marks to disappear completely.

4. **Treat yourself to a body mask.** Most aesthetic salons offer a mud pack treatment using algae or mud over the whole body. A good home treatment would be to bathe in either the toxin eliminator bath, or in 30 grams of either micronized marine algae or sea salts add the essential oils of Grapefruit and Cypress, 3 drops of each.

5. **Carry on with a good balanced diet.** The more nutritional food and the less rubbish one eats, the better the body will function. I would advise anyone who is on a diet to keep the ratio of weight loss to 1-2 pounds a week and not to crash diet in order to avoid the above problem.

Hand Care

Ageing shows up first on the hands, we can have face lifts and look ten years younger, but, we cannot have hand lifts yet. Therefore we must take care of our skin on our hands. One of the biggest giveaways of ageing is the sign of big brown spots on the back of our hands. Here is a little more information to help combat those brown critters.

The medical name for brown spots, liver spots or age spots is *lentigos.* These marks are caused by free radicals in the body and can be promoted by a combination of ultraviolet radiation and perfumes or eau de colognes *(most perfumes contain some form of photosensitizer, such as bergamot).* There are external and internal aids that help in the reduction of *lentigos.*

For example, the use of lemon essential oil is helpful. Make your own external treatment oil by adding 5 drops lemon essential oil to 15ml of almond oil or basic white lotion. Apply daily, preferably at night.

Another external remedy is made with fresh pineapple juice which contains an enzyme called *bromelain.* Dab some juice on the spots and leave it on for twenty minutes and then rinse it off.

Caution: Do not use lemon essential oil on the hands before sunbathing or when doing outside activities.

For internal remedies, vitamin E used along with vitamin C has been known to decrease age spots. Foods that contain vitamin E are leafy vegetables such as cabbage, spinach and broccoli, whole grain foods such as rice, wheat and oats, vegetable oils, especially wheat germ oil, plus eggs and liver. Vitamin C is found in citrus fruits, green peppers, broccoli. spinach and tomatoes.

For general hand care, here is a good general hand cream especially good for chapped, dry skin.

Calendula Hand Cream

To 30ml of the calendula base cream, add the essential oils of sandalwood and orange, 5 drops of each.

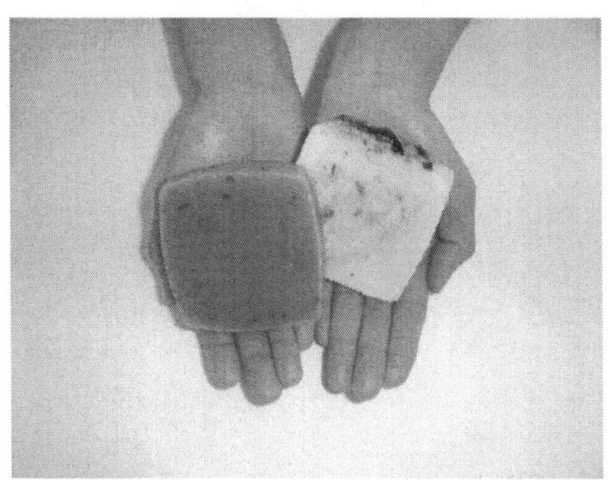

Eri Nose presenting Aroma Soaps

BAD HAIR DAY

Stress, both physical and psychological, and nutritional imbalance can affect the hair. When the body is under a lot of stress, the first thing that will suffer is the externals: hair, skin and nails. This is part of the body's natural protective mechanism which will direct nutrients in the body to the most vital areas.

If you are suffering prematurely greying and thinning hair or your hair has just lost its natural gloss, read on. Aside from dealing with stress through relaxation and massage therapy, one plan of attack is through nutrition. The plan of attack through nutritional therapy is divided into two areas; Vitamins/Herbs and Diet.

There are vitamins especially for anti-stress:
Vitamin C, suggested daily intake - 1,000mg

B complex vitamins 50 -75 mg

Calcium and Magnesium supplements 800mg/400mg

Even more specifically, there are vitamins and herbs which attack the problem of thinning hair itself.

Lecithin, suggested daily intake - 1,200mg.
Herbs such as Kelp, Nettle, Dandelion and Alfalfa all seem to help as well.

Taking silica helps to thicken hair; this is found in the herb horsetail.

Please check with your health professional for dosages that are suitable for you

Make the necessary dietary changes. One aspect can be the balancing of Acid and Alkaline levels in the body.

We have been discussing internal approaches to this problem of thinning hair but external remedies are also available. Treat thinning hair with the following formula.

Hair tonic

The following hair tonic helps with hair loss, thinning hair and general condition.

To a pump spray container containing 50ml of witch hazel, add the following essential oils:

Cedarwood 5 drops
Juniper berry 10 drops
Rosemary 15 drops.

Apply a small amount to the scalp morning and night. Massage scalp at the same time by gluing fingertips to skin of the scalp and rotating the skin over the bone.

Follow the directions given and you should see an improvement within 3 months.

For treatment of the general condition of the hair, you can simply add essential oils to your shampoo and/or to treatment 1 or 2.

Oily hair....Add Geranium, Lemon, and/or Rosemary.

Dry hair.....Add Chamomile, Sandalwood and/or Lavender

Dandruff....Add Rosemary, Lemon and/or Lavender

Shampoo: To your favourite shampoo, add 10-20 drops of essential oil/s

Treatment 1: To 10ml of Jojoba oil, add 8-12 drops of essential oil/s.

I like the following mix for shiny, glossy hair: 3 drops Rosemary, 3 drops lavender, 4 drops lemon, 2 drops Sandalwood.

After shampooing and half-drying your hair, apply the oil mix to the scalp by massaging. Wrap your hair in a very hot towel; then, cover with a plastic bag. Take a hot shower or bath, after 20 minutes remove the plastic bag and towel. Let the residue dry in your hair overnight, shampoo in the morning, if necessary.

Treatment 2: To 25ml of witch hazel and 25ml of purified water, add 10-20 drops of essential oil/s. Use as per hair tonic.

In addition, some general tips are to be gentle with your hair by using a comb (not a brush) when the hair is wet and by a careful choice of products.

PART FIVE
The Art of Seduction or Cleopatra's Secrets.

Now we come almost to the end of this book, what you have all been waiting for.

Follow this guide, it is the secret of many a seductress to use essential oils. They do affect the endocrine glands of both yourself and the people around you. Essential oils also affect how you feel about yourself; if the right buttons are pushed so to speak, you will let out the right vibes for men to look at you. Yes it can happen that you can suddenly have gorgeous men stop and stare and treat you as the desirable woman that you are. It is nothing to do with your facial features or body type; it is the sexual vibes that you give off.

With the following essential oils, you will feel sexy, move sensuously, and as a result be a sexual being.

So enough of this, let's get now so to speak to the nitty, gritty of life.

Follow this five point plan of action

- Skin brush
- Bath in the exotic bath mix. *See page 76*
- Moisturise with a basic white lotion or Jojoba oil with an added exotic blend.
- Dust with the body powder containing ylang ylang or a drop of jasmine and add a little powdered lepidolite crystal. *See page 78*

- Dress in your favourite outfit and look at yourself in the mirror, eye to eye and say nine times, I am beautiful, sexy and desired by all men. (Watch out, it does work).

RECIPES

Add to 30g of bath salts, 30ml of body lotion or jojoba oil and 30g of dusting powders, any of the following exotic blends.

Exotic blend no 1

Essential oils:

Ylang ylang 5 drops

Jasmine 1 drop

Mandarin 5 drops

Exotic blend no 2

Essential oils:

Patchouli 2 drops

Neroli 4 drops

Ylang ylang 5 drops

Exotic blend no 3

Essential oils:

Linden Blossom 5 drops

Jasmine 3 drops

Basil 2 drops.

A Good Night's Sleep

To let the spirit wander through time and space
the never ending cosmos; a swirling place
Oh what a pleasure to be given this gift
to enter this realm of joy and bliss

by Jan Benham.

To have a beautiful, clear skin, a good night's sleep is important. If you are having problems falling off to sleep have a bath with the following essential oils.

Marjoram 2 drops
Lavender 2 drops
Ylang ylang 2 drops

Mix into 5ml of sweet almond oil or oil of choice, and massage into your body. Then, soak in the bath for at least 10 minutes.

An alternative would be to place 6 drops of the essential oil blend onto a tissue, place tissue across the face and breathe in the vapours until sleep comes. The mix can also be added to an electrical diffuser.

Your notes and recipes

Your notes and recipes

Bibliography and Further Reading

Some of the books which I have referred to over the last few years, and for whose existence, I am very grateful.

Aromatherapy Handbook Erich Keller

Aromatherapy for Women Maggie Tisserand

Practical Aromatherapy Shirley Price

The Aromatherapy Book Jeanne Rose

The Aromatherapy Workbook Shirley Price

The Art of Aromatherapy Robert Tisserand

The Baby Boomer's Beauty Bible Jan Benham

The Little Book of Lipsticks Jan Benham

The Practice of Aromatherapy Dr. Jean Valnet

Index

If you enjoyed this book, check out the other books by the author.

The Baby Boomers Beauty Bible, 2004 contains tips on how to keep your skin looking healthy and youthful with easy user-friendly recipes for various anti-ageing treatments and skin problems.
Presented with straightforward advice for body care that includes suggestions to soothe the soul and stimulate the mind.
Included in this book are more recipes for skin care, natural deodorants, hair shampoos and conditioners.

The little Book of lipsticks, 2010 is a fun but practical book, which contains easy to follow recipes to make safe, all natural, professional quality lipsticks.
Included is the history and trivia of lipsticks, knowledge of the natural ingredients used, and how to apply the perfect lipstick.
Recipes included are: Baby pink, Cinnamon girl, Smitten and Chocolate kisses *(made with real chocolate).*

Coming soon: The Art of Soap Making, 2011 and The Art of Making Natural Makeup, 2012